TUNES for TWO

TUNES for TWO

Easy Duets for Violins

**Thirty popular melodies
arranged by
Christopher Tambling**

Kevin
Mayhew

We hope you enjoy the music in *Tunes for Two*.
Further copies of this and the other books in the series
are available from your local music shop.

In case of difficulty, please contact the publisher direct:

The Sales Department
KEVIN MAYHEW LTD
Rattlesden
Bury St Edmunds
Suffolk IP30 0SZ

Phone 0449 737978
Fax 0449 737834

Please ask for our complete catalogue of outstanding Instrumental Music.

First published in Great Britain in 1994 by Kevin Mayhew Ltd

ISBN 0 86209 545 X
Catalogue No: 3611116

All or part of these pieces have been arranged by Christopher Tambling
and are the copyright of Kevin Mayhew Ltd.

Cover Design by Bob Bond
Music Editor: Anthea Smith
Music setting by Louise Hill

Printed and bound in Great Britain

Contents

Arranger's Note

Tunes for Two is a collection of thirty well-known pieces arranged as instrumental duets. These pieces can be used in a variety of different ways – they might serve as a useful introduction to ensemble playing; they could be used as sight-reading pieces during a music lesson; or they could be enjoyed simply as fun pieces at home or school. There is no distinction between 'pupil' and 'teacher' parts – players should feel free to swop lines!

The aim of this book is to provide duet material for players of approximately Grades 1 to 3 standard, starting with simpler pieces and progressing towards more challenging arrangements at the end of the book. I hope that *Tunes for Two* will be enjoyed by players of all ages and abilities.

CHRISTOPHER TAMBLING

ALL on D + A STRINGS

For Sara

TALLIS'S CANON

Thomas Tallis

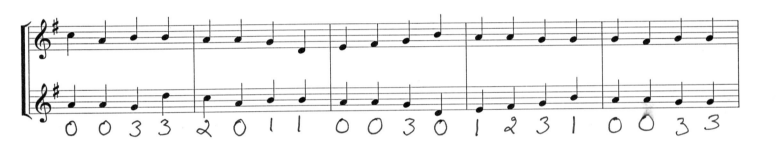

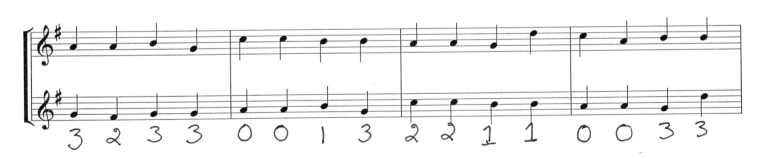

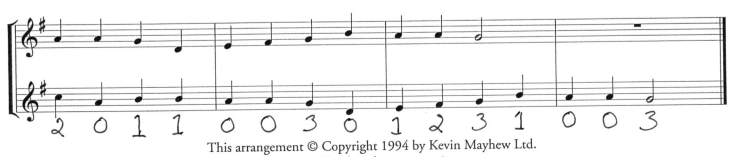

ALL ON A EXCEPT for 2 notes !!! on E

WHEN THE SAINTS GO MARCHING IN

Spiritual

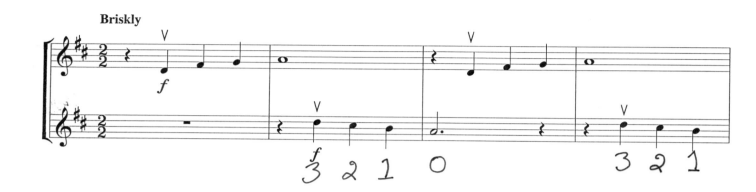

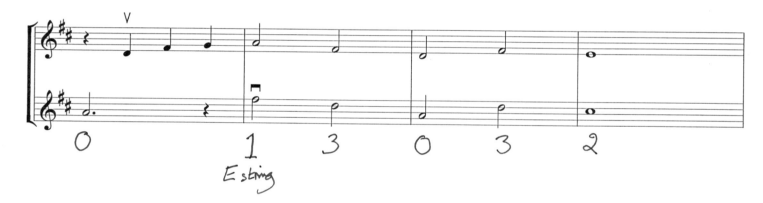

E string

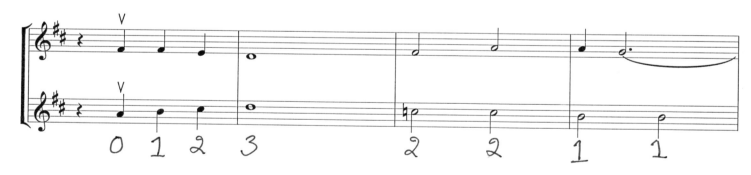

E string

ALL ON A EXCEPT for 3 notes on D

ALL THROUGH THE NIGHT

Traditional Welsh Melody

WERE YOU THERE?

Spiritual

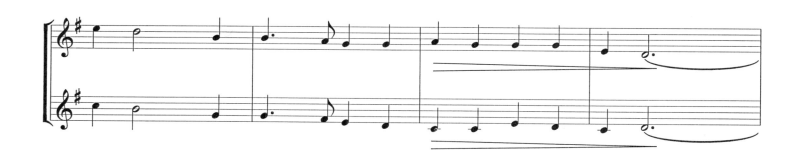

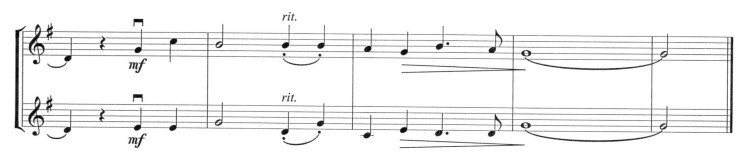

This arrangement © Copyright 1994 by Kevin Mayhew Ltd.
It is illegal to photocopy music.

ODE TO JOY

Ludwig Van Beethoven

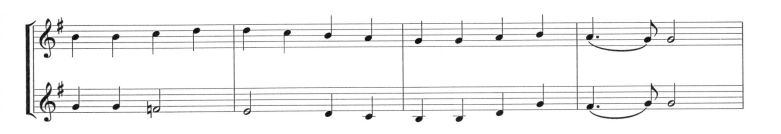

PASSION CHORALE

Hans Leo Hassler

Not too fast

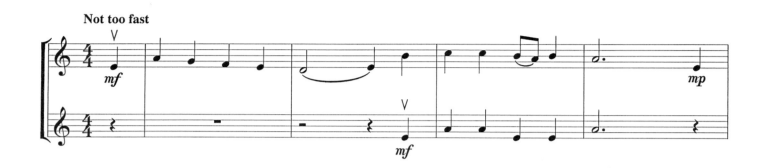

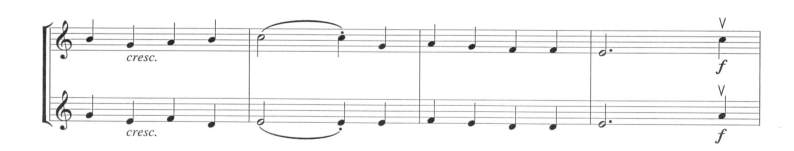

STEAL AWAY

Spiritual

ALL IN A GARDEN GREEN

Traditional English Melody

SPRING

Antonio Vivaldi

SKYE BOAT SONG

Traditional Scottish Melody

16

SOLDIERS' MARCH

Robert Schumann

BIST DU BEI MIR

Johann Sebastian Bach

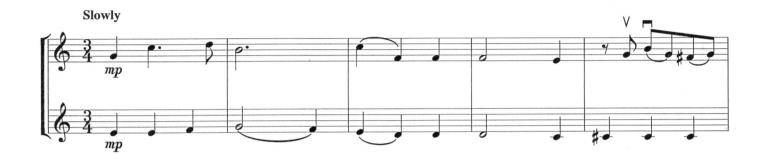

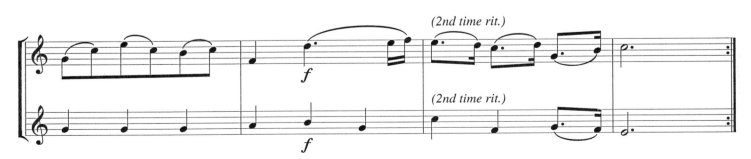

BOURRÉE

George Frideric Handel

LARGO

Antonín Dvořák

PAVAN
16th Century Melody

This arrangement © Copyright 1994 by Kevin Mayhew Ltd.
It is illegal to photocopy music.

MINUET

George Frideric Handel

Allegro pomposo

This arrangement © Copyright 1994 by Kevin Mayhew Ltd.
It is illegal to photocopy music.

IMPROMPTU

Franz Schubert

Andante

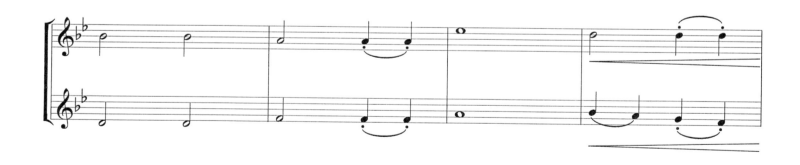

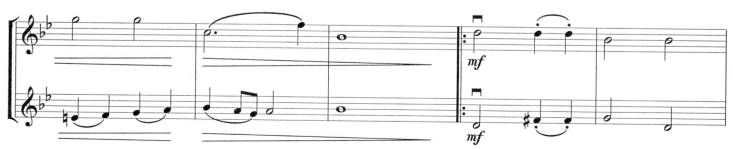

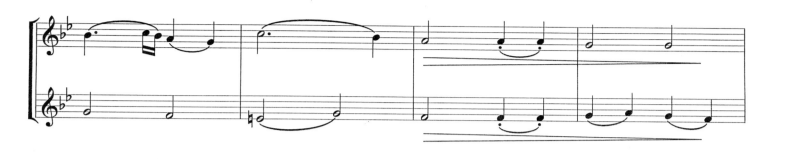

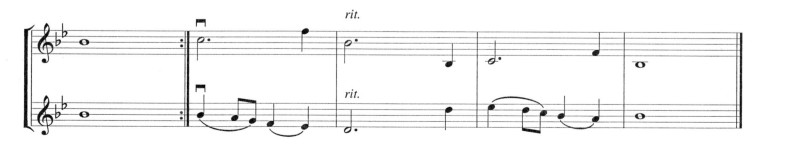

AUTUMN

Antonio Vivaldi

THE SILVER SWAN

Orlando Gibbons

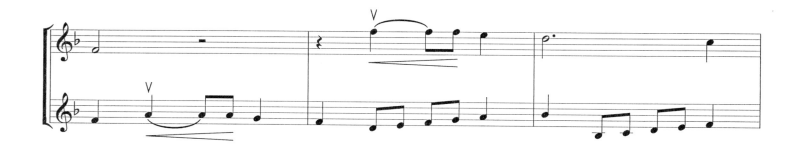

29

MARCHE MILITAIRE

Franz Schubert

31

MINUET
Wolfgang Amadeus Mozart

GREENSLEEVES

16th Century Melody

TRUMPET VOLUNTARY

Jeremiah Clarke

Allegro vivace

TO A WILD ROSE

Edward MacDowell

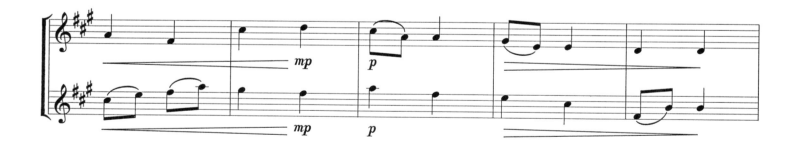

MARCH

George Frideric Handel

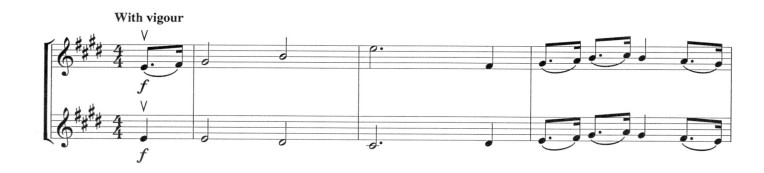

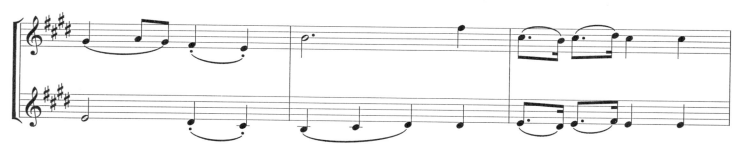

PAPAGENO'S ARIA

Wolfgang Amadeus Mozart

MY BONNY LASS SHE SMILETH

Thomas Morley

THE ENTERTAINER

Scott Joplin

NON PIÙ ANDRAI

Wolfgang Amadeus Mozart

COUNTRY GARDENS

Traditional English Melody